TOSEL®

READING SERIES

STARTER

READING 1

International TOSEL Committee

CONTENTS

About TOSEL®

TOSEL (Test of Skills in the English Language) was developed to meet the demand for a more effective assessment of English as a foreign language for learners from specific cultural settings.

TOSEL evaluates and certifies the proficiency levels of English learners, from the age of 4 through adulthood, along with academic and job performance results.

Background

- Other English tests are ineffective in accurately measuring individual abilities
- Overuse of US-dominated testing systems in diverse cultural and educational contexts in the global English language learning market

Functions & Usage

- Assessment is categorized into 7 levels
- Used as a qualification for academic excellence for school admissions
- Used as a test to assess the English proficiency in the corporate and public sectors

Goals

- Create an effective tool for assessing and evaluating the English skills of English language learners
- Implement efficient and accessible testing systems and methods
- Provide constructive and developmental English education guidance

TOSEL® Strength

LEVELED ASSESSMENTS

An established English test system fit for seven different levels according to learners' cognitive development

ACCURATE DIAGNOSIS

A systematic and scientific diagnosis of learners' English proficiency

EXTENSIVE MATERIALS

Supplementary materials to help learners in an EFL environment to prepare for TOSEL and improve their proficiency

SUFFICIENT DATA

Content for each level developed by using data accumulated from more than 2,000,000 TOSEL test takers delegated at 15,000 schools and academies

CLASSIFIED AREAS OF INTELLIGENCE

Content designed to foster and expand the strengths of each student, categorized by the eight areas of intelligence

CONTINUITY

A complete course of English education ranging from kindergarten, elementary school, middle school, high schoool, and up to adults.

HIGH RELIABILITY

A high reliability level (Cronbach's alpha: .904 for elementary school students / .864 for university students) proven by several studies (Oxford University / Modern Language Journal)

SYSTEMATIC & EFFECTIVE ENGLISH EDUCATION

Accurate diagnosis and extensive materials which provide a step-by-step development in English learning, according to the quality of each learner's ability

TOSEL® Level Chart

Seven Separate Assessments

TOSEL divides the test into seven stages, by considering the test takers' cognitive levels, according to different ages. Unlike other assessments based on only one level, TOSEL includes separate assessments for preschool, elementary school, middle school, high school students, and for adults, which also includes both professionals and college students.

TOSEL's reporting system highlights the strengths and weaknesses of each test taker and suggests areas for further development.

COCOON

Suitable for children aged 4-6 (pre-schoolers)

The first step in the TOSEL system, the test is composed of colorful designs and interesting questions to interest young learners and to put them at ease.

Pre-STARTER

Suitable for children aged 7-8 (1st-2nd grades of elementary school)

Evaluates the ability to comprehend simple vocabulary, conversations, and sentences.

STARTER

Suitable for children aged 9-10 (3rd-4th grades of elementary school)

Evaluates the ability to comprehend short sentences and conversations related to everyday situations or topics.

BASIC

Suitable for children aged 11-12 (5th–6th grades of elementary school)

Evaluates the ability to communicate about personal information, daily activities, future plans, and past experiences in written and spoken language.

JUNIOR

Suitable for middle school students

Evaluates the ability to comprehend short paragraphs, practical texts, and speech covering general topics and to participate in simple daily conversations.

HIGH JUNIOR

Suitable for high school students

Evaluates the ability to use English fluently, accurately, and effectively on a wide range of social and academic subjects, as well as the ability to use sentences with a variety of complex structures.

ADVANCED

Suitable for university students and adults

Evaluates the ability to use practical English required for a job or work environment, as well as the ability to use and understand English at the university level.

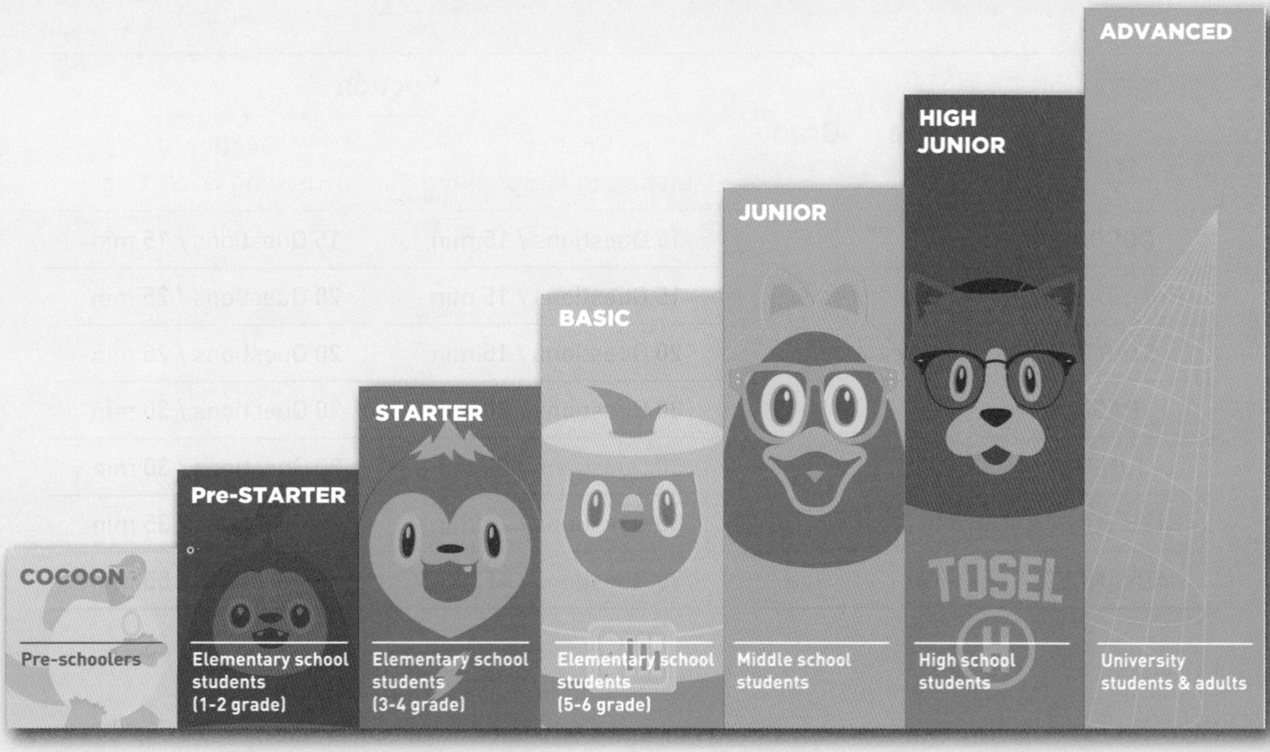

Evaluation

Assessing the Four Skills

TOSEL evaluates the four language skills: reading, listening, speaking and writing, through indirect and direct assessment items.

This system of evaluation is part of a concerted effort to break away from materials geared solely toward grammar and reading-oriented education.

TOSEL Test Information

Level	Score	Grade	Section	
			Section I Listening & Speaking	Section II Reading & Writing
COCOON	100		15 Questions / 15 min	15 Questions / 15 min
Pre-STARTER	100		15 Questions / 15 min	20 Questions / 25 min
STARTER	100		20 Questions / 15 min	20 Questions / 25 min
BASIC	100	1-10	30 Questions / 20 min	30 Questions / 30 min
JUNIOR	100		30 Questions / 20 min	30 Questions / 30 min
HIGH JUNIOR	100		30 Questions / 25 min	35 Questions / 35 min
ADVANCED	990		70 Questions / 45 min	70 Questions / 55 min

Certificates

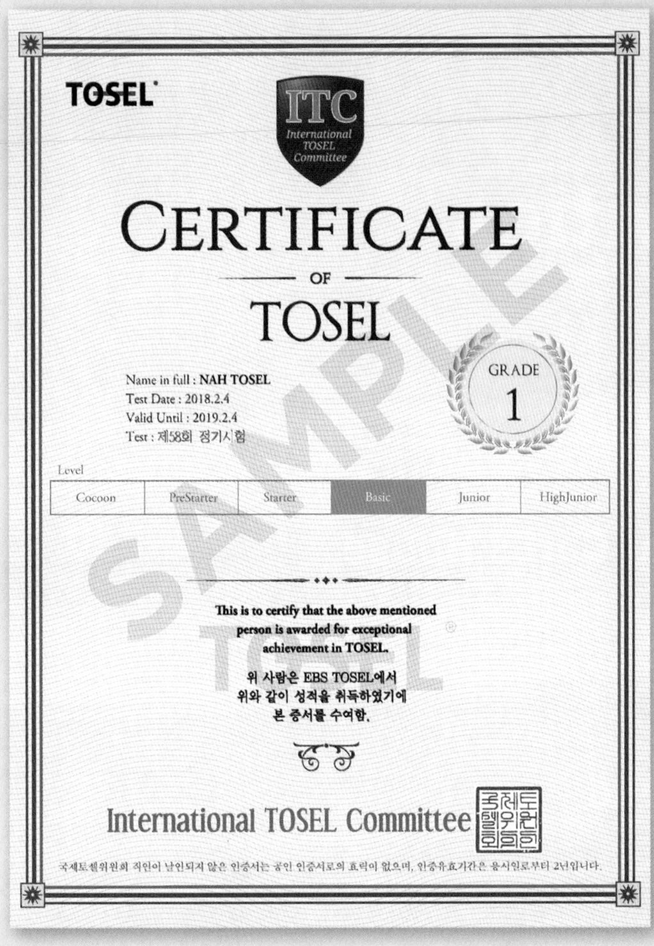
TOSEL

ITC International TOSEL Committee

CERTIFICATE OF TOSEL

Name in full : NAH TOSEL
Test Date : 2018.2.4
Valid Until : 2019.2.4
Test : 제58회 정기시험

GRADE 1

Level

Cocoon	PreStarter	Starter	Basic	Junior	HighJunior

This is to certify that the above mentioned person is awarded for exceptional achievement in TOSEL.

위 사람은 EBS TOSEL에서 위와 같이 성적을 취득하였기에 본 증서를 수여함.

International TOSEL Committee

SAMPLE

TOSEL Certificate

The International TOSEL Committee officially evaluates and certifies the level of English proficiency of English learners from the age of 4 to adults.

Certified by

Mar. 2010 Korea University
Dec. 2009 The Korean Society of Speech Science
Dec. 2009 The Korea Association of Foreign Language Education
Nov. 2009 The Applied Linguistics Association of Korea
Oct. 2009 The Pan Korea English Teachers Association

CHAPTER 1

Weekend Activities

Teacher's Book
p.44

UNIT 1

Sarah's Strange Night

When do you wake up? Draw the time.
When do you go to sleep? Draw the time.

UNIT 1 Sarah's Strange Night

It is 9 o'clock at night. Sarah goes to bed. Tomorrow is a big day. She must wake up at 7 AM. Sarah goes to sleep. Then she wakes up. She looks at the clock. She screams. It is 10 o'clock! She is late! Sarah moves fast. She takes a shower. Then she dries her hair. She packs her bag. She looks out the window. But it is dark outside. Why is it dark? It is 10 o'clock at night! Sarah shakes her head. She goes to her room.

New Words

wake up

scream

pack a bag

dry

10 minutes

Part A. Sentence Completion

1. He shakes ________ head.

    (A) he
    (B) his
    (C) him
    (D) he's

2. She ________ to sleep.

    (A) go
    (B) goes
    (C) to go
    (D) going

Part B. Situational Writing

3. 

Sarah ________ her hair in her room.

(A) ties
(B) cuts
(C) dries
(D) brushes

4. 

He ________ his bag for school.

(A) buys
(B) packs
(C) colors
(D) washes

Part C. Practical Reading and Retelling

Before Berko Goes to Bed

5. What does Berko do at 9:00?

(A) eat dinner
(B) brush teeth
(C) do homework
(D) take a shower

6. When does Berko run?

(A) at 5:30
(B) at 6:10
(C) at 8:00
(D) at 10:00

Part D. General Reading and Retelling

It is 9 o'clock at night. Sarah goes to bed. Tomorrow is a big day. She must wake up at 7 AM. Sarah goes to sleep. Then she wakes up. She looks at the clock. She screams. It is 10 o'clock! She is late! Sarah moves fast. She takes a shower. Then she dries her hair. She packs her bag. She looks out the window. But it is dark outside. Why is it dark? It is 10 o'clock at night! Sarah shakes her head. She goes to her room.

7. What is the best title?

(A) A Bright Day
(B) Sarah's Night
(C) A Big New Bag
(D) Sarah Cleans Her Room

8. At what time does Sarah go to bed?

(A) 9 AM
(B) 9 PM
(C) 10 AM
(D) 10 PM

9. Why does Sarah scream?

(A) She is late.
(B) She sees a bug.
(C) Her bag is gone.
(D) The shower is cold.

10. What does Sarah NOT do after she wakes up?

(A) run outside
(B) dry her hair
(C) pack her bag
(D) take a shower

Listening Practice

Listen and write.

MP3 S1-1

Sarah's Strange Night

It is 9 o'clock at night. Sarah goes to bed. Tomorrow is a big day. She must 1 ____________ at 7 AM. Sarah goes to sleep. Then she wakes up. She looks at the clock. She 2 ____________. It is 10 o'clock! She is late! Sarah moves fast. She takes a shower. Then she 3 ____________ her hair. She 4 ____________ her bag. She looks out the window. But it is dark outside. Why is it dark? It is 10 o'clock at night! Sarah shakes her head. She goes to her room.

Word Bank

dries	packs
screams	paks
scrims	wakeup
wake up	drys

Listen. Pause. Say each sentence.

MP3 S1-1G

Writing Practice

Write the words.

1 ☐☐☐☐ ☐☐

2 ☐☐☐☐☐☐

3 ☐☐☐☐ ☐ ☐☐☐

4 ☐☐☐

Write the words.

Summary

Sarah ________________ at 9 PM. She must wake up at 7 AM. But she wakes up at 10. It is 10 PM!

Word Puzzle

D	N	P	H	D	J	O	C	Z	O	Q	A	P	P	P
I	Y	E	B	R	N	N	S	W	D	D	Q	B	D	Q
F	Y	M	O	Y	C	R	C	T	U	D	X	O	C	H
Z	I	Z	C	J	S	C	R	Q	M	Q	J	Q	H	I
O	R	E	F	U	F	X	E	L	I	I	T	O	N	Q
R	C	S	M	J	M	P	A	C	K	A	B	A	G	T
N	M	R	G	R	D	N	M	V	P	G	T	U	X	Y
U	Y	K	N	Y	R	G	G	G	L	M	Q	X	W	V
M	O	L	E	Z	Q	S	J	P	K	O	O	N	A	G
I	R	M	X	M	G	Y	Q	R	I	P	G	L	K	Y
H	A	O	L	K	O	R	X	Z	U	M	Q	G	E	M
W	S	Y	O	E	E	C	Z	I	U	I	V	K	U	E
H	V	O	K	Z	A	G	X	A	R	D	S	Q	P	X
Y	G	X	X	D	N	G	G	N	V	C	Z	R	C	V
U	B	Z	R	V	L	V	O	G	I	F	T	Z	V	F

Write the words. Then find them in the puzzle.

1 ____________________

2 ____________________

3 ____________________

4 ____________________

Teacher's Book p.47

UNIT 2

Sunday Morning at Carl's House

How many people are in your family?
Do you have any sisters or brothers?
If so, how many?

UNIT 2 Sunday Morning at Carl's House

Today is Sunday. It is a sunny morning. Carl's family is in the living room. Carl's father is watching TV. He is lying on the sofa. Carl's mother is wearing headphones. She is listening to her favorite music. Carl is hungry. He goes to the kitchen. There is no food. So he bakes cookies. Carl's sister is in the garden. She likes taking photos. She takes photos of flowers. Suddenly, the phone rings. Carl's father answers the phone. He says, "Hello." Then he calls Carl. He says, "Carl, your school friend wants you! Come here."

New Words

phone

headphones

bake

take photos
(of something)

10 minutes

Part A. Sentence Completion

1. There ________ no food.

(A) is
(B) be
(C) am
(D) can

2. His father ________ TV.

(A) watch
(B) is watch
(C) watches
(D) watching

Part B. Situational Writing

3.

Carl's mother is wearing ________.

(A) a hat
(B) a scarf
(C) earrings
(D) headphones

4.

Let's take pictures in the ________.

(A) gym
(B) garden
(C) kitchen
(D) living room

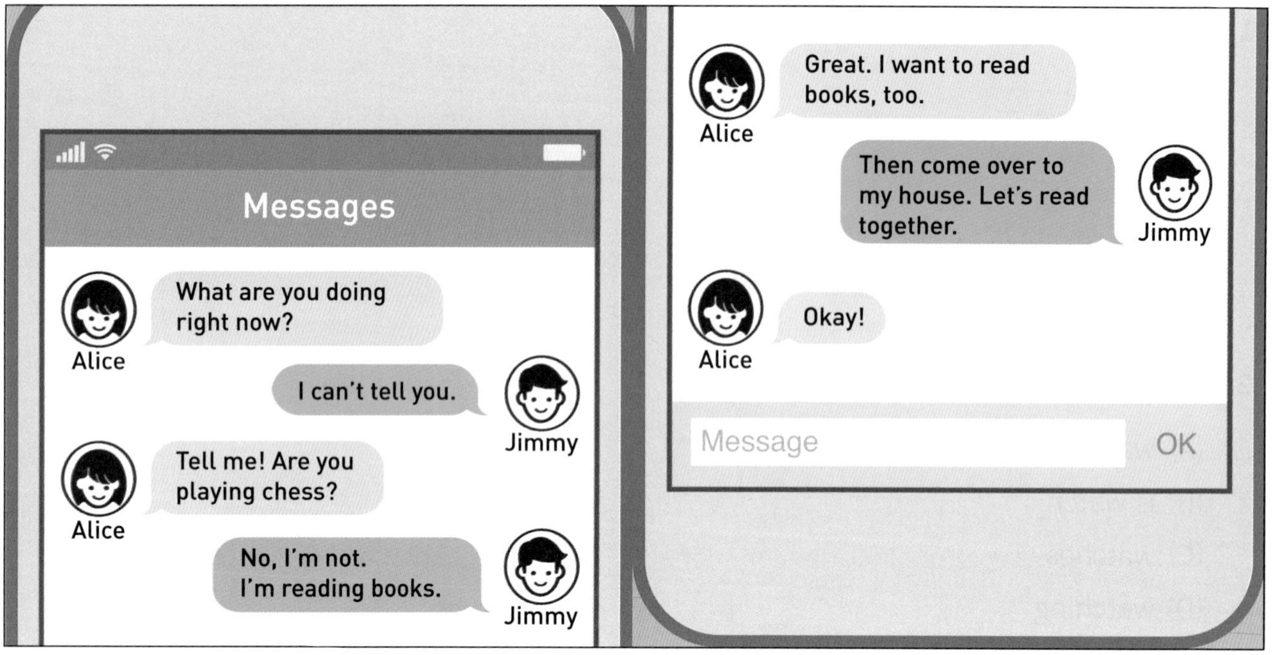

5. What is Jimmy doing now?

(A) taking a walk
(B) taking photos
(C) playing chess
(D) reading books

6. Where is Alice going?

(A) to school
(B) to her room
(C) to the hospital
(D) to Jimmy's house

Part D. General Reading and Retelling

Today is Sunday. It is a sunny morning. Carl's family is in the living room. Carl's father is watching TV. He is lying on the sofa. Carl's mother is wearing headphones. She is listening to her favorite music. Carl is hungry. He goes to the kitchen. There is no food. So he bakes cookies. Carl's sister is in the garden. She likes taking photos. She takes photos of flowers. Suddenly, the phone rings. Carl's father answers the phone. He says, "Hello." Then he calls Carl. He says, "Carl, your school friend wants you! Come here."

7. What is the best title?
   (A) Baking Class
   (B) Walking in the Park
   (C) Carl's Friends at School
   (D) Carl's Family on Sunday

8. What is Carl's mother doing?
   (A) lying on the sofa
   (B) listening to music
   (C) answering the phone
   (D) taking photos of flowers

9. Why does Carl bake cookies?
   (A) He is cold.
   (B) He is hungry.
   (C) His friend is visiting.
   (D) His mother wants cookies.

10. Who is on the phone?
   (A) Carl's sister
   (B) Carl's friend
   (C) Carl's teacher
   (D) Carl's grandfather

Listening Practice

Listen and write.

MP3 S1-2

Sunday Morning at Carl's House

Today is Sunday. It is a sunny morning. Carl's family is in the living room. Carl's father is watching TV. He is lying on the sofa. Carl's mother is wearing [1] ____________. She is listening to her favorite music. Carl is hungry. He goes to the kitchen. There is no food. So he [2] ____________ cookies. Carl's sister is in the garden. She likes taking [3] ____________. She takes photos of flowers. Suddenly, the phone rings. Carl's father answers the [4] ____________. He says, "Hello." Then he calls Carl. He says, "Carl, your school friend wants you! Come here."

Word Bank

photos	headpones
phone	headphones
baks	pone
bakes	fotos

Listen. Pause. Say each sentence.

MP3 S1-2G

Writing Practice

Write the words.

1

2

3

4

Write the words.

Summary

It is ________________ morning. Carl's family is in the living room. Carl's friend calls.

Word Puzzle

J	V	Z	H	P	S	Q	F	Y	K	S	P	I	E	M
H	K	U	E	Q	A	L	T	Z	I	K	H	Q	F	Y
P	O	M	A	Z	Y	J	S	K	B	U	E	G	C	Q
U	I	Z	D	A	S	P	R	E	P	M	G	B	Y	L
I	G	O	P	P	B	I	E	E	S	N	V	G	L	Z
A	U	S	H	Q	N	Y	Y	I	X	L	G	X	X	B
G	K	M	O	B	H	I	K	S	W	K	A	N	P	Z
O	C	N	N	X	U	K	M	G	P	B	Z	E	R	S
L	V	M	E	T	P	H	O	N	E	H	Q	C	Z	M
Q	O	H	S	R	M	C	J	Y	H	D	K	G	J	X
W	U	S	F	B	W	A	M	V	X	Z	F	A	H	N
O	W	V	M	W	T	A	K	E	P	H	O	T	O	S
Z	P	S	X	N	N	T	K	L	D	X	V	P	M	G
W	W	D	A	L	Z	G	N	P	O	M	J	A	N	A
Y	Z	Y	G	A	Z	E	R	B	A	K	E	Q	X	P

Write the words. Then find them in the puzzle.

1 ______________ 2 ______________ 3 ______________ 4 ______________

Teacher's Book p.51

UNIT 3

A Field Trip

Does your school have field trips?
Where does your class go on field trips?

UNIT 3 A Field Trip

What starts on June 26? It is Boram Elementary School's big field trip! The trip is two days. On the first day, Class 1 goes fishing. Students wait for a big fish, but no fish bites. Class 2 goes hiking. The class goes up a big mountain. The students like the fresh air. But they are very hot. On day 2, both classes ride on horses. They go to a hill and learn about safety. They all wear helmets. They ride the horses. It is so much fun! How does the trip end? There is a cooking contest. Class 1 makes a pepperoni pizza. Class 2 makes pasta with tomato sauce. Class 2 wins the contest. The students are all happy.

New Words

fresh

hill

safety

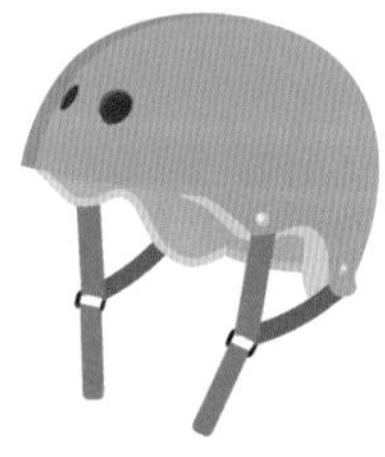

helmet

10 minutes

Part A. Sentence Completion

1. What starts ________ June 26?

(A) in
(B) on
(C) above
(D) behind

2. I ________ the fresh air here.

(A) like
(B) liker
(C) likes
(D) liking

Part B. Situational Writing

3.

The rider wears a ________.

(A) skirt
(B) mask
(C) dress
(D) helmet

4.

Our class wins the ________ contest.

(A) hiking
(B) fishing
(C) driving
(D) cooking

Welcome to Wonder Water Land!

Here are the water sports on Thursday and Friday.

What?	How much?	How long?	Where?
Surfing	$100	30 minutes	Gate A
Sailing	$120	40 minutes	Gate B
Water skiing	$150	25 minutes	Gate C

5. What can we do at Gate C?

(A) sailing
(B) surfing
(C) rowing
(D) water skiing

6. What is NOT true about sailing?

(A) It is at Gate B.
(B) One hour costs $120.
(C) It is open on Thursday.
(D) You can sail for 40 minutes.

Part D. General Reading and Retelling

What starts on June 26? It is Boram Elementary School's big field trip! The trip is two days. On the first day, Class 1 goes fishing. Students wait for a big fish, but no fish bites. Class 2 goes hiking. The class goes up a big mountain. The students like the fresh air. But they are very hot. On day 2, both classes ride on horses. They go to a hill and learn about safety. They all wear helmets. They ride the horses. It is so much fun! How does the trip end? There is a cooking contest. Class 1 makes a pepperoni pizza. Class 2 makes pasta with tomato sauce. Class 2 wins the contest. The students are all happy.

7. What is the best title?

(A) Final Exam
(B) Hiking Lessons
(C) Cook and Travel
(D) School Field Trip

8. When does the field trip end?

(A) June 26th
(B) June 27th
(C) July 26th
(D) July 27th

9. What do Class 1 students do on the first day?

(A) go fishing
(B) ride horses
(C) catch a big fish
(D) climb a mountain

10. What is true about the second day?

(A) Both classes go to a hill.
(B) Both classes make pasta.
(C) Class 1 and 2 do not meet.
(D) The cooking contest has no winner.

Listening Practice

Listen and write.

MP3 S1-3

A Field Trip

What starts on June 26? It is Boram Elementary School's big field trip! The trip is two days. On the first day, Class 1 goes fishing. Students wait for a big fish, but no fish bites. Class 2 goes hiking. The class goes up a big mountain. The students like the [1] ________ air. But they are very hot. On day 2, both classes ride on horses. They go to a [2] ________ and learn about [3] ________. They all wear [4] ________. They ride the horses. It is so much fun! How does the trip end? There is a cooking contest. Class 1 makes a pepperoni pizza. Class 2 makes pasta with tomato sauce. Class 2 wins the contest. The students are all happy.

Word Bank

helmuts	safty
hill	helmets
safety	hil
presh	fresh

Listen. Pause. Say each sentence.

MP3 S1-3G

Writing Practice

Write the words.

1

2

3

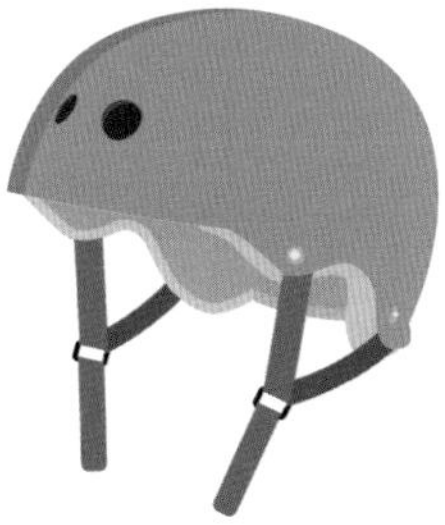

4

Write the words.

Summary

Boram Elementary School has a big ______________. The students fish, hike, and ride on horses. There is a cooking contest.

Word Puzzle

B	F	N	U	Q	E	Y	K	I	P	O	Q	F	D	N
R	B	N	Q	Q	M	Z	Q	V	N	N	N	M	K	O
F	V	Z	N	X	A	A	U	D	X	O	S	I	Q	R
F	R	E	S	H	V	C	D	W	B	S	U	P	Z	T
O	W	H	S	H	N	I	H	W	L	O	D	L	P	L
H	N	M	X	C	R	X	B	F	S	A	F	E	T	Y
I	K	G	A	Q	T	J	Z	A	S	R	K	F	Y	W
L	G	J	H	Y	Q	F	G	P	X	A	J	J	M	G
L	V	I	R	P	E	C	C	H	E	L	M	E	T	V
M	B	S	K	P	L	K	J	W	X	L	X	R	S	P
N	X	P	G	J	F	A	T	T	G	H	U	E	L	O
B	S	P	L	J	T	I	H	T	C	H	H	E	M	N
P	X	L	R	L	V	D	L	S	B	R	S	D	P	V
B	Q	I	S	D	G	R	Z	W	F	M	O	X	Z	R
C	X	V	I	N	N	P	U	O	M	P	Z	L	E	C

Write the words. Then find them in the puzzle.

1 ____________

2 ____________

3 ____________

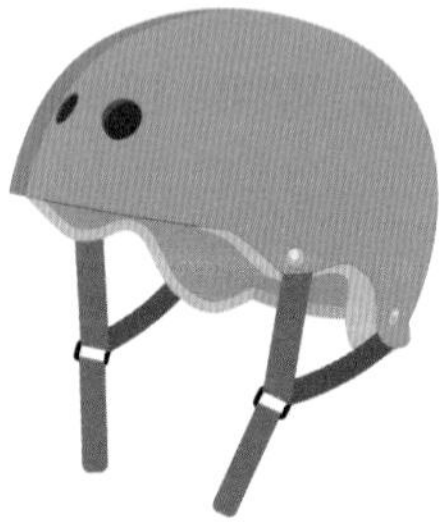

4 ____________

Teacher's Book
p.55

UNIT 4

Zoe's Busy Weekend

Here are three weekend plans.
Which is the best for you?

1) watching a movie
2) playing outside
3) going to an amusement park

UNIT 4 Zoe's Busy Weekend

Why is Zoe excited right now? Because it is the weekend! Zoe is planning her weekend now. She is writing her schedule in the diary. On Saturday, Zoe is going to the movie theater. She is watching an action movie. She likes to watch movies alone. Her favorite movie theater is downtown. After the movie, she is taking the subway downtown. Then, Zoe is going back home. There, she is having dinner with her family. On Sunday, Zoe is going to an amusement park with her sister. She likes the roller coaster. But on Sundays, the amusement park always has many people. Zoe and her sister have to wake up early on Sunday. The weekend is busy. But it is fun.

New Words

diary

movie theater

subway

amusement park

10 minutes

Part A. Sentence Completion

1. ________ the weekend busy?

(A) Is
(B) Do
(C) Can
(D) Where

2. She is ________ her weekend.

(A) plan
(B) plans
(C) planner
(D) planning

Part B. Situational Writing

3.

Zoe plans her weekend in her ________.

(A) diary
(B) palm
(C) email
(D) phone

4.

They take the ________ to get to the theater.

(A) boat
(B) truck
(C) plane
(D) subway

5. What is this ticket for?

(A) a piano concert
(B) a baseball game
(C) a basketball match
(D) a party for sports players

6. What is true about this ticket?

(A) It is for two people.
(B) It costs 15,000 won.
(C) It is only for Koreans.
(D) It is for Seoul Stadium.

Part D. General Reading and Retelling

Why is Zoe excited right now? Because it is the weekend! Zoe is planning her weekend now. She is writing her schedule in the diary. On Saturday, Zoe is going to the movie theater. She is watching an action movie. She likes to watch movies alone. Her favorite movie theater is downtown. After the movie, she is taking the subway downtown. Then, Zoe is going back home. There, she is having dinner with her family. On Sunday, Zoe is going to an amusement park with her sister. She likes the roller coaster. But on Sundays, the amusement park always has many people. Zoe and her sister have to wake up early on Sunday. The weekend is busy. But it is fun.

7. What is Zoe excited about?

(A) a big concert
(B) a busy weekend
(C) her summer vacation
(D) her grandparents' visit

8. What is Zoe doing now?

(A) taking the subway
(B) riding a roller coaster
(C) planning her weekend
(D) watching an action movie

9. On Saturday, what is Zoe doing with her family?

(A) watching TV
(B) eating dinner
(C) writing in her diary
(D) going to the theater

10. What is Zoe doing on Sunday?

(A) having a picnic
(B) doing her homework
(C) watching an action movie
(D) going to an amusement park

Listening Practice

Listen and write.

MP3 S1-4

Zoe's Busy Weekend

Why is Zoe excited right now? Because it is the weekend! Zoe is planning her weekend now. She is writing her schedule in the [1] __________. On Saturday, Zoe is going to the [2] __________ theater. She is watching an action movie. She likes to watch movies alone. Her favorite movie theater is downtown. After the movie, she is taking the [3] __________ downtown. Then, Zoe is going back home. There, she is having dinner with her family. On Sunday, Zoe is going to an [4] __________ park with her sister. She likes the roller coaster. But on Sundays, the amusement park always has many people. Zoe and her sister have to wake up early on Sunday. The weekend is busy. But it is fun.

Word Bank

amusement	amusemnt
diarry	diary
movie	subway
sabway	mobie

Listen. Pause. Say each sentence.

MP3 S1-4G

Writing Practice

Write the words.

1

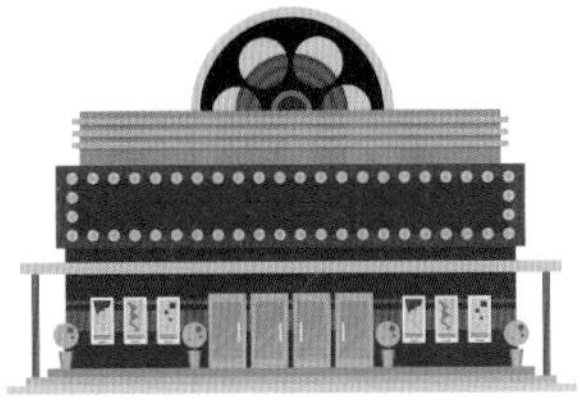

2

3

4

Write the words.

Summary

Zoe has a busy weekend. She is going to a ________________ and having a family dinner. On Sunday, she is going to an amusement park.

Word Puzzle

Q	K	R	A	F	D	N	H	Y	L	X	J	X	H	H
O	E	T	M	M	O	V	M	Q	S	K	G	G	E	P
H	A	H	F	O	D	V	O	M	Z	F	K	R	J	R
P	M	Y	X	V	K	L	H	U	I	N	D	P	R	O
W	U	M	X	I	Y	D	X	R	L	B	A	C	K	D
U	S	D	Z	E	U	I	Z	A	S	L	W	F	Z	B
Q	E	N	D	T	G	A	E	E	S	X	Y	O	U	B
C	M	U	G	H	W	R	Z	Y	E	J	M	M	N	U
F	E	U	B	E	W	Y	K	O	R	X	H	V	Y	X
S	N	K	Q	A	D	E	J	X	J	G	R	N	L	R
H	T	C	R	T	A	T	K	R	T	I	Q	F	Q	O
D	P	T	Y	E	H	Y	U	L	I	C	F	V	T	S
I	A	Z	P	R	B	J	J	E	N	X	Q	B	O	T
V	R	Q	X	B	F	E	F	I	W	B	A	V	T	F
M	K	X	S	U	B	W	A	Y	M	K	W	O	R	R

Write the words. Then find them in the puzzle.

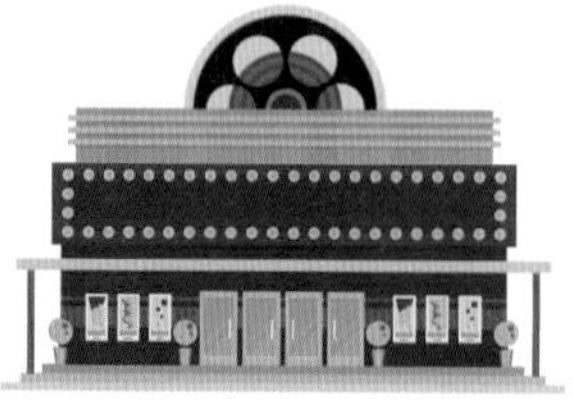

1 ____________ 2 ____________ 3 ____________ 4 ____________

CHAPTER REVIEW

Match the pictures to the correct words.

Teacher's Book p.59

amusement park
bake
diary
dry
fresh
headphones
helmet
hill
movie theater
pack a bag
phone
safety
scream
subway
take photos
wake up

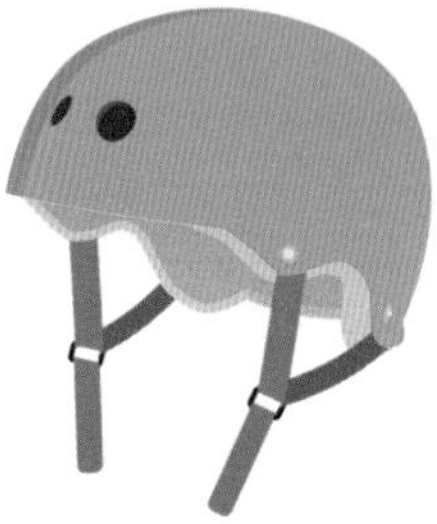

CHAPTER 2

Find Out about Your Friends

Teacher's Book p.60

UNIT 5

All about Pumpkins

Draw a face on the pumpkin.
Is the face funny, happy, or sad, or scary?

UNIT 5 All about Pumpkins

What are pumpkins? Are they vegetables? No, they are not. Pumpkins are fruit. Pumpkins are round, like a ball. And they have thick shells. What color are they? Many pumpkins are orange. But there are white pumpkins and even green ones! Pumpkins can have different sizes. Some are tiny. Many are around 6 kilograms. But some pumpkins become very, very big. Some pumpkins are over 800 kilograms! How do people eat pumpkins? Some people like pumpkin salad. Others like pumpkin soup. Pumpkins are also for holidays. Often on Halloween, some people cut pumpkins. They give the pumpkins faces. They put candles in the pumpkins. On Thanksgiving and Christmas, many people eat pumpkin pie.

New Words

pumpkin

shell

vegetable

holiday

10 minutes

Part A. Sentence Completion

1. ________ do people eat pumpkins?

   (A) Who
   (B) How
   (C) What
   (D) Which

2. Those pumpkins ________ orange.

   (A) is
   (B) are
   (C) does
   (D) doing

Part B. Situational Writing

3. 

   Watermelons are ________, like a ball.

   (A) red
   (B) soft
   (C) round
   (D) square

4. 

   Put a ________ in the pumpkin!

   (A) pie
   (B) shell
   (C) knife
   (D) candle

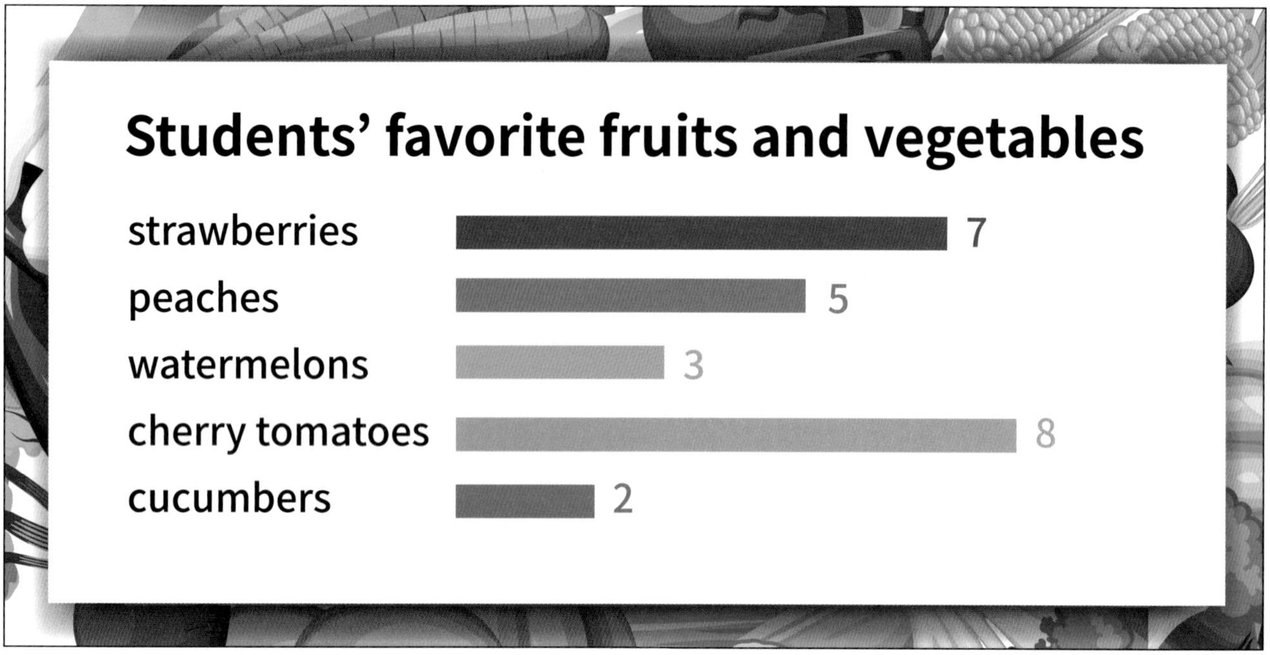

5. How many students like watermelons?

(A) 2
(B) 3
(C) 7
(D) 8

6. What is the most popular fruit or vegetable?

(A) peaches
(B) cucumbers
(C) strawberries
(D) cherry tomatoes

Part D. **General Reading and Retelling**

What are pumpkins? Are they vegetables? No, they are not. Pumpkins are fruit. Pumpkins are round, like a ball. And they have thick shells. What color are they? Many pumpkins are orange. But there are white pumpkins and even green ones! Pumpkins can have different sizes. Some are tiny. Many are around 6 kilograms. But some pumpkins become very, very big. Some pumpkins are over 800 kilograms! How do people eat pumpkins? Some people like pumpkin salad. Others like pumpkin soup. Pumpkins are also for holidays. Often on Halloween, some people cut pumpkins. They give the pumpkins faces. They put candles in the pumpkins. On Thanksgiving and Christmas, many people eat pumpkin pie.

7. What is the best title?

(A) Great Holidays
(B) Food for Animals
(C) Baking Fruit Cakes
(D) All about Pumpkins

8. Which is NOT a pumpkin color?

(A) blue
(B) white
(C) green
(D) orange

9. What is true about many pumpkins?

(A) They look like rectangles.
(B) They have different sizes.
(C) They have very thin shells.
(D) They are over 900 kilograms.

10. When do pumpkins often get faces?

(A) on Christmas
(B) on Halloween
(C) on Thanksgiving
(D) on New Year's Day

Listening Practice

Listen and write.

MP3 S1-5

All about Pumpkins

What are [1] ____________ ? Are they [2] ____________ ? No, they are not. Pumpkins are fruit. Pumpkins are round, like a ball. And they have thick [3] ____________ . What color are they? Many pumpkins are orange. But there are white pumpkins and even green ones! Pumpkins can have different sizes. Some are tiny. Many are around 6 kilograms. But some pumpkins become very, very big. Some pumpkins are over 800 kilograms! How do people eat pumpkins? Some people like pumpkin salad. Others like pumpkin soup. Pumpkins are also for [4] ____________ . Often on Halloween, some people cut pumpkins. They give the pumpkins faces. They put candles in the pumpkins. On Thanksgiving and Christmas, many people eat pumpkin pie.

Word Bank

holliday	shells
shels	vegetables
begetables	pampkins
holidays	pumpkins

Listen. Pause. Say each sentence.

MP3 S1-5G

Writing Practice

Write the words.

1

2

3

4

Write the words.

Summary

__________________ are round, thick fruits. They have different sizes, and many of them are orange. People eat pumpkin soup and salad. Some people use pumpkins for holidays.

Word Puzzle

R	N	S	H	E	L	L	X	Q	F	K	P	W	H	P
S	Q	T	J	Y	L	T	V	H	E	N	U	Q	V	Y
I	N	S	J	B	B	A	E	B	I	J	M	E	D	X
N	E	O	Y	S	Y	S	G	I	T	F	P	W	P	P
K	S	M	H	E	K	L	E	C	B	I	K	G	O	P
B	W	S	Z	S	J	V	T	H	D	Y	I	U	U	T
C	R	Y	X	F	C	E	A	C	B	S	N	J	R	Z
M	O	Z	D	C	Z	E	B	V	R	L	K	N	B	Y
P	N	O	Q	A	H	O	L	I	D	A	Y	H	H	J
E	T	N	V	T	I	A	E	L	X	W	I	R	U	G
V	Q	Y	P	F	D	B	E	T	E	N	C	H	Q	P
Y	O	D	Y	T	V	I	D	I	D	P	G	H	U	W
E	A	W	S	M	D	N	U	X	U	Z	F	U	Z	J
M	N	C	E	R	T	Z	Y	H	L	A	F	Y	F	B
Y	U	L	T	H	G	X	O	X	T	H	H	Y	W	C

Write the words. Then find them in the puzzle.

1 ______________

2 ______________

3 ______________

4 ______________

Teacher's Book p.64

UNIT 6

Chores at Home

Which chores do you do at home?

UNIT 6 Chores at Home

Eric's family does many things at home. Eric's father waters the plants. He has to wake up early. Why? He waters the plants each morning. What does Eric's mother do? She feeds the dog. She also walks the dog. They walk near the house. Then Eric's parents make breakfast together. Sometimes they make eggs and toast. Sometimes they make chicken and rice. Eric and his sister also have to cook something. That is the family rule. Today Eric and his sister make onion soup. After breakfast, Eric's sister washes the dishes. Eric sweeps the floor. Eric's father folds the laundry. And Eric's mother takes out the trash. They have to do so many things at home!

New Words

feed

sweep

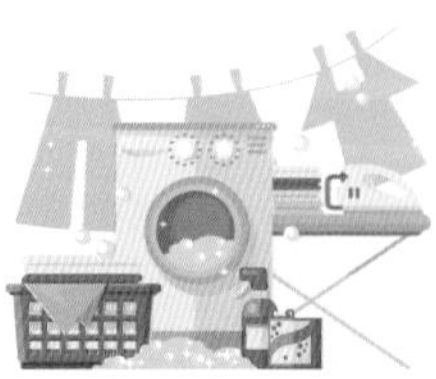
laundry

trash

Part A. Sentence Completion

1. ________ makes breakfast? My father makes breakfast.

(A) Who
(B) Why
(C) What
(D) Where

2. What ________ his mother do? She feeds the dog.

(A) is
(B) are
(C) do
(D) does

Part B. Situational Writing

3. 

Eric's father ________ the plants in the garden.

(A) cuts
(B) eats
(C) dries
(D) waters

4. 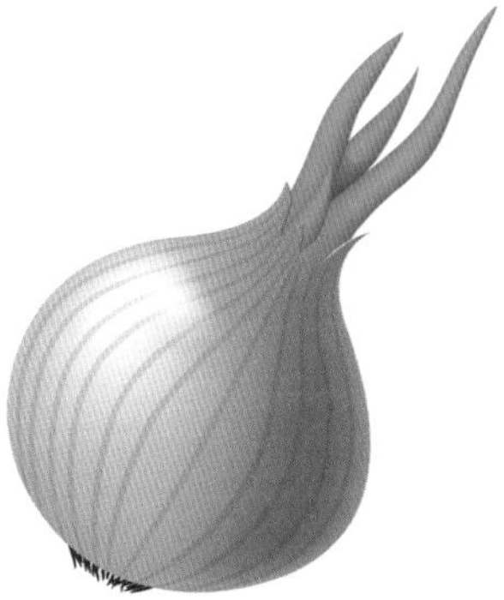

We need a large ________ for the soup.

(A) onion
(B) carrot
(C) pumpkin
(D) mushroom

Part C. Practical Reading and Retelling

Kimberly,

Tonight we are coming home late. We're sorry.

There is a tomato sandwich on the kitchen table.
And there is some soup on the stove.
Please eat the soup and sandwich for dinner. Then, wash the dishes.
Please go to sleep before 9.

Have sweet dreams, daughter! We love you.

XOXOX
Mom and Dad

5. Who is the letter from?

   (A) Kimberly
   (B) Kimberly's friend
   (C) Kimberly's parents
   (D) Kimberly's neighbors

6. What does Kimberly NOT have to do?

   (A) eat dinner
   (B) wash the dishes
   (C) go to sleep before 9
   (D) make a tomato sandwich

Part D. General Reading and Retelling

Eric's family does many things at home. Eric's father waters the plants. He has to wake up early. Why? He waters the plants each morning. What does Eric's mother do? She feeds the dog. She also walks the dog. They walk near the house. Then Eric's parents make breakfast together. Sometimes they make eggs and toast. Sometimes they make chicken and rice. Eric and his sister also have to cook something. That is the family rule. Today Eric and his sister make onion soup. After breakfast, Eric's sister washes the dishes. Eric sweeps the floor. Eric's father folds the laundry. And Eric's mother takes out the trash. They have to do so many things at home!

7. What is the best title?
   (A) Eric's Big Vacation
   (B) Sleeping in the Garden
   (C) Sitting in the Living Room
   (D) Many Things to Do at Home

8. What does Eric's father do?
   (A) feed the dog
   (B) walk the dog
   (C) make breakfast
   (D) wash the dishes

9. Who sweeps the floor?
   (A) Eric
   (B) Eric's sister
   (C) Eric's father
   (D) Eric's mother

10. What does Eric's sister do today?
   (A) sweep the floor
   (B) water the plants
   (C) make onion soup
   (D) take out the trash

Listening Practice

Listen and write.

MP3 S1-6

Chores at Home

Eric's family does many things at home. Eric's father waters the plants. He has to wake up early. Why? He waters the plants each morning. What does Eric's mother do? She [1] ________ the dog. She also walks the dog. They walk near the house. Then Eric's parents make breakfast together. Sometimes they make eggs and toast. Sometimes they make chicken and rice. Eric and his sister also have to cook something. That is the family rule. Today Eric and his sister make onion soup. After breakfast, Eric's sister washes the dishes. Eric [2] ________ the floor. Eric's father folds the [3] ________. And Eric's mother takes out the [4] ________. They have to do so many things at home!

Word Bank

laundry	swips
fids	tresh
trash	feeds
sweeps	londry

Listen. Pause. Say each sentence.

MP3 S1-6G

Writing Practice

Write the words.

1

2

3

4

Write the words.

Summary

Eric's family does many things at ________________. They water plants, take care of the dog, and make breakfast. They wash dishes, sweep the floor, fold laundry, and take out the trash.

Word Puzzle

Z	W	H	Q	I	T	B	J	K	E	O	L	G	S	Z
K	Z	B	I	E	K	G	X	H	Q	P	Y	G	W	T
P	S	B	I	Y	R	U	X	S	Z	U	T	A	E	U
H	L	J	J	N	K	Q	K	X	U	X	K	Z	E	X
T	R	A	S	H	U	F	D	H	D	G	D	G	P	V
X	S	L	T	S	K	Q	H	K	N	F	H	D	A	H
N	K	Z	B	H	K	T	T	J	V	O	X	F	P	T
Q	B	P	C	G	F	O	U	W	X	A	P	E	N	M
K	G	A	Q	E	E	M	B	P	U	V	I	E	B	T
D	M	B	L	J	L	D	W	L	A	U	N	D	R	Y
T	C	V	L	I	W	U	H	A	P	Q	J	N	C	L
E	H	N	P	Y	D	K	L	Q	B	P	I	M	U	Y
Z	X	F	S	L	L	G	B	M	I	Q	Z	I	J	E
P	W	Q	X	Y	H	A	U	M	Z	C	P	B	Y	J
F	C	D	S	K	U	O	L	B	Y	V	O	T	C	X

Write the words. Then find them in the puzzle.

1 ______________

2 ______________

3 ______________

4 ______________

Teacher's Book p.68

UNIT 7

Having a Party

Think! It is your birthday. Who is at the party?
Is there food? If so, what kind?
Are there presents? If so, what are they?

Having a Party

Today is a very special day. It is Nora's birthday. Nora's friends are planning a party. The birthday party is at Nora's house. Her friends do many things. First, they buy birthday gifts. They get a fancy pen and pencil for Nora. Nora likes to write. So she needs pens and pencils. Second, Nora's friends make special foods. They make cookies. Cookies are Nora's favorite dessert. What drinks are at the party? There are lemonade and orange juice. Also, Nora's friends make birthday cards. And they hang balloons. The balloons are many colors. There are red, yellow, green, and blue balloons. And Nora's friends put on party hats. Now, everything is ready. Nora's friends wait for Nora.

New Words

plan

fancy

put on

wait for

10 minutes

Part A. Sentence Completion

1. They ________ gifts.

(A) buy
(B) buys
(C) is buy
(D) is to buy

2. It is ________ birthday.

(A) I
(B) he
(C) we
(D) her

Part B. Situational Writing

3.

Do you like ________?

(A) milk
(B) coffee
(C) lemonade
(D) apple juice

4.

Nora loves ________.

(A) robots
(B) pencils
(C) cookies
(D) oranges

Dear Tom,
Nick is turning 7!
Come and enjoy his birthday party.

- Wednesday, March 24th
- 2 PM to 4 PM
- Nick's house is on 3100 Abbey Road.

5. Who gets this card?

(A) Tom
(B) Nick
(C) Abbey
(D) March

6. What is NOT on the card?

(A) Nick's age
(B) Nick's road
(C) Nick's house number
(D) Nick's phone number

Part D. General Reading and Retelling

Today is a very special day. It is Nora's birthday. Nora's friends are planning a party. The birthday party is at Nora's house. Her friends do many things. First, they buy birthday gifts. They get a fancy pen and pencil for Nora. Nora likes to write. So she needs pens and pencils. Second, Nora's friends make special foods. They make cookies. Cookies are Nora's favorite dessert. What drinks are at the party? There are lemonade and orange juice. Also, Nora's friends make birthday cards. And they hang balloons. The balloons are many colors. There are red, yellow, green, and blue balloons. And Nora's friends put on party hats. Now, everything is ready. Nora's friends wait for Nora.

7. What is the best title?
   (A) After the Party
   (B) Nora's Parents
   (C) Balloons in the House
   (D) Preparing for the Party

8. What is the party for?
   (A) Christmas
   (B) Thanksgiving
   (C) Nora's birthday
   (D) Nora's wedding

9. What is NOT at the party?
   (A) cookies
   (B) popcorn
   (C) balloons
   (D) lemonade

10. What does Nora like to do?
   (A) shop
   (B) draw
   (C) write
   (D) color

Listening Practice

Listen and write.

MP3 S1-7

Having a Party

Today is a very special day. It is Nora's birthday. Nora's friends are 1 ____________ a party. The birthday party is at Nora's house. Her friends do many things. First, they buy birthday gifts. They get a 2 ____________ pen and pencil for Nora. Nora likes to write. So she needs pens and pencils. Second, Nora's friends make special foods. They make cookies. Cookies are Nora's favorite dessert. What drinks are at the party? There are lemonade and orange juice. Also, Nora's friends make birthday cards. And they hang balloons. The balloons are many colors. There are red, yellow, green, and blue balloons. And Nora's friends 3 ____________ party hats. Now, everything is ready. Nora's friends 4 ____________ for Nora.

Word Bank

fency	planing
put on	planning
fancy	wait
puton	weit

Listen. Pause. Say each sentence.

MP3 S1-7G

Writing Practice

Write the words.

1

2

3

4

Write the words.

Summary

Today is Nora's birthday. Nora's friends are planning a ______________ at Nora's house. Her friends buy gifts, bake cookies, and make birthday cards. They hang balloons and put on party hats.

Word Puzzle

F	A	N	C	Y	I	S	M	V	R	S	S	W	V	H
K	F	N	X	I	N	B	J	F	S	H	A	A	V	X
V	C	D	F	K	G	D	Q	S	S	G	G	I	R	V
L	M	P	H	O	F	E	S	Q	M	X	B	T	C	R
H	K	P	K	F	T	P	M	I	X	D	N	F	D	C
D	Q	L	P	F	S	F	E	P	Y	F	O	O	V	B
X	X	Y	A	D	W	U	F	W	O	Y	L	R	R	Y
Y	S	G	G	P	U	L	P	Z	J	U	I	Q	J	I
T	N	W	B	M	P	I	W	J	S	V	Q	J	W	N
K	D	H	G	M	L	D	A	X	D	A	J	D	D	H
U	W	E	F	R	A	Z	Z	A	H	V	L	G	X	H
W	P	U	T	O	N	K	M	M	L	X	V	B	E	M
E	T	D	I	F	T	O	G	V	N	L	L	V	H	O
S	G	G	C	E	A	F	R	X	A	L	J	G	D	A
L	L	D	S	U	Q	P	R	X	D	H	O	P	R	D

Write the words. Then find them in the puzzle.

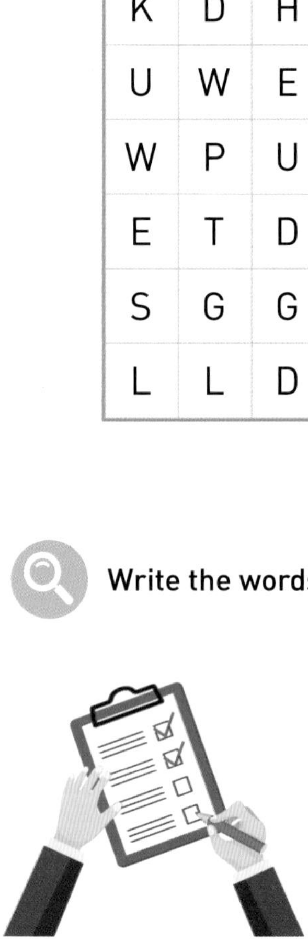

1 ____________

2 ____________

3 ____________

4 ____________

Teacher's Book
p.72

UNIT 8

Kelly Learns Chinese Sounds

Can you speak Chinese?
Can you speak English?
Can you speak Spanish?

UNIT 8 Kelly Learns Chinese Sounds

Kelly is in Chinese class now. She is a new learner. The class is very hard. Why is it hard? There are special sounds. These sounds are called "tones." Kelly knows the first and second tone. What is today's class? It is about the third tone. The third tone has two parts. First it falls. Then it goes up again. Kelly cannot do the third tone well. She is sad. Why are there tones? The tones make new words. The teacher says "*ma*". He uses the first tone. It means "mother." Then he says "*ma*" in the third tone. It means "horse." Kelly practices the sounds all afternoon. Tomorrow, she is learning the last tone. It is the fourth tone!

New Words

first

second

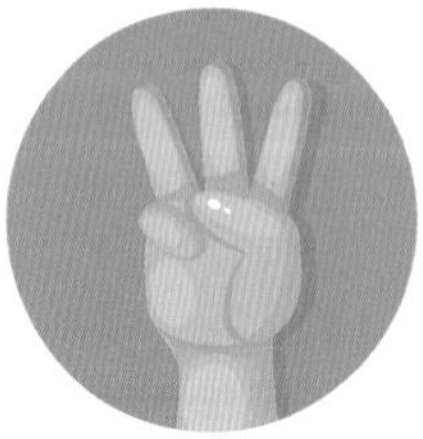

third

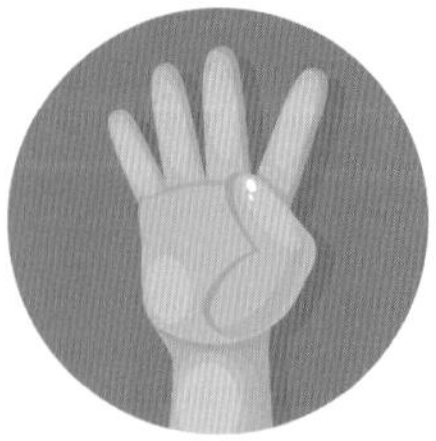

fourth

10 minutes

Part A. Sentence Completion

1. This word ________ very hard.

(A) is
(B) do
(C) are
(D) make

2. It has two ________.

(A) part
(B) parts
(C) a part
(D) is a part

Part B. Situational Writing

3.

The yellow car is ________.

(A) first
(B) second
(C) third
(D) fourth

4.

My birthday is on August ________.

(A) first
(B) second
(C) third
(D) fourth

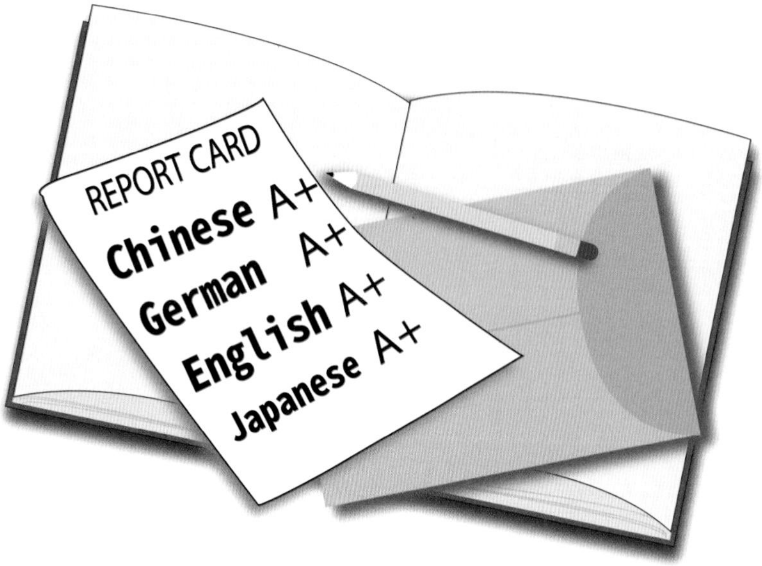

Teacher's note:

Ella, great job.
You always study hard.

5. What does Ella NOT learn?

(A) French
(B) English
(C) German
(D) Japanese

6. What does Ella's teacher say?

(A) Ella studies hard.
(B) Ella is always late.
(C) Ella hates learning.
(D) Ella needs a new job.

Part D. General Reading and Retelling

Kelly is in Chinese class now. She is a new learner. The class is very hard. Why is it hard? There are special sounds. These sounds are called "tones." Kelly knows the first and second tone. What is today's class? It is about the third tone. The third tone has two parts. First it falls. Then it goes up again. Kelly cannot do the third tone well. She is sad. Why are there tones? The tones make new words. The teacher says "*ma*". He uses the first tone. It means "mother." Then he says "*ma*" in the third tone. It means "horse." Kelly practices the sounds all afternoon. Tomorrow, she is learning the last tone. It is the fourth tone!

7. What is the best title?

(A) Chinese Horses
(B) Four Hard Words
(C) Kelly Learns Tones
(D) Kelly Teaches English

8. Which is the third tone?

(A) 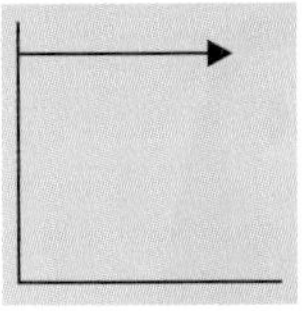
(B) 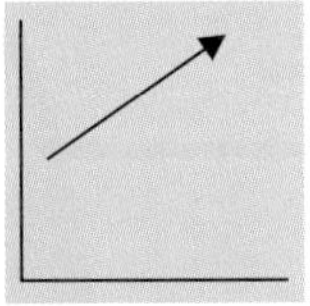
(C) 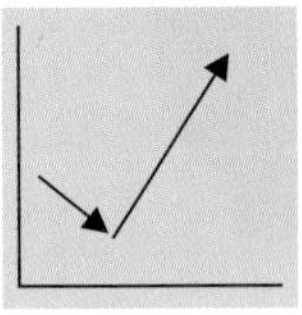
(D) 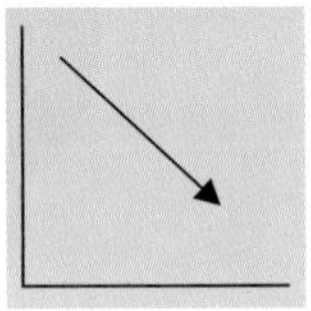

9. What does "*ma*" mean in the third tone?

(A) Kelly
(B) horse
(C) China
(D) mother

10. Which is true?

(A) Kelly knows three tones.
(B) Kelly is learning Japanese.
(C) Kelly knows the fourth tone.
(D) Kelly is in class with her mother.

Listening Practice

Listen and write.

MP3 S1-8

Kelly Learns Chinese Sounds

Kelly is in Chinese class now. She is a new learner. The class is very hard. Why is it hard? There are special sounds. These sounds are called "tones." Kelly knows the [1] ______________ and [2] ______________ tone. What is today's class? It is about the [3] ______________ tone. The third tone has two parts. First it falls. Then it goes up again. Kelly cannot do the third tone well. She is sad. Why are there tones? The tones make new words. The teacher says "*ma*". He uses the first tone. It means "mother." Then he says "*ma*" in the third tone. It means "horse." Kelly practices the sounds all afternoon. Tomorrow, she is learning the last tone. It is the [4] ______________ tone!

Word Bank

first	third
fourse	fourth
pirst	thud
sicond	second

Listen. Pause. Say each sentence.

MP3 S1-8G

Writing Practice

Write the words.

1 ☐☐☐☐☐

2 ☐☐☐☐☐☐

3 ☐☐☐☐☐

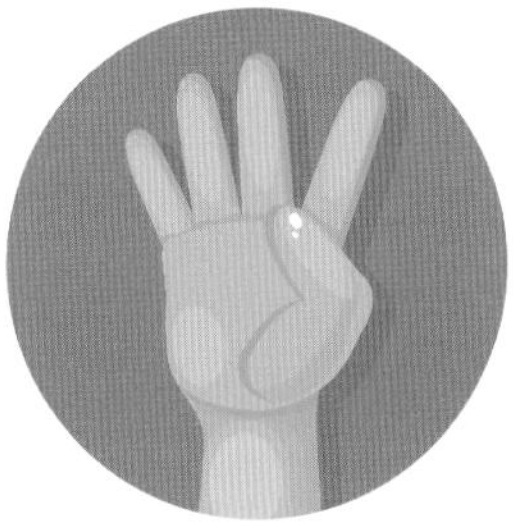

4 ☐☐☐☐☐☐

Write the words.

Summary

Kelly is learning Chinese. It is hard for Kelly. There are special ________________s called 'tones'. Kelly practices the tones.

Word Puzzle

A	W	D	O	G	G	W	S	B	G	B	T	I	R	U
N	B	O	W	L	K	F	S	P	D	A	V	N	Q	Z
N	Q	T	D	F	W	K	A	Z	S	F	U	X	L	O
V	M	M	F	N	L	B	F	X	E	B	Z	F	L	L
L	H	Y	I	T	K	A	T	K	C	F	P	A	N	O
A	R	L	R	B	T	T	E	M	O	X	C	S	A	Q
Q	E	G	S	V	C	H	O	R	N	R	Y	O	G	C
F	D	R	T	M	E	M	J	V	D	C	N	D	S	E
V	O	G	Z	C	B	R	V	C	B	Z	Y	B	W	U
I	C	B	I	T	G	F	L	R	Z	N	G	X	V	V
F	R	L	U	H	G	L	H	R	Y	J	Q	Q	O	G
V	T	V	M	I	S	N	J	A	B	V	X	W	M	L
L	F	O	U	R	T	H	O	L	U	C	B	Z	V	T
F	Q	O	M	D	T	J	M	C	F	C	W	A	J	Z
C	M	J	E	D	H	I	J	O	S	M	V	S	H	Y

Write the words. Then find them in the puzzle.

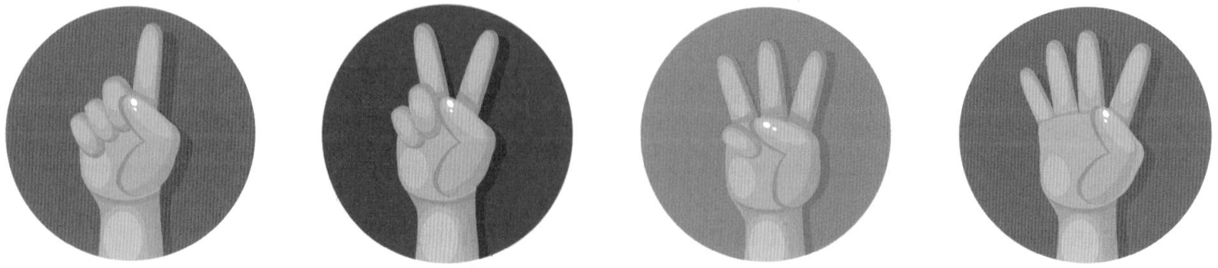

1 ______ 2 ______ 3 ______ 4 ______

CHAPTER REVIEW

Match the pictures to the correct words.

Teacher's Book p.76

fancy
feed
first
fourth
holiday
laundry
plan
pumpkin
put on
second
shell
sweep
third
trash
vegetable
wait for

CHAPTER 3

Ask More Questions

Teacher's Book p.77

UNIT 9

Andrea Loves Sports

What are your favorite sports?
How often do you play them?

UNIT 9 Andrea Loves Sports

Andrea wants to be a sports player. Does she like only one sport? No, she loves many sports! She loves badminton, baseball, and swimming. She practices sports every day. She plays baseball three times a week. Every Monday, Wednesday, and Friday, she goes to the school playground. She carries a baseball glove and a ball. She is a baseball pitcher. She plays badminton twice a week. Where is she on Tuesdays and Thursdays? She is at the badminton court. She brings her racket. What about Saturday? Saturday is swimming day. She goes to the pool near her school. She always wears swimming goggles. Every Sunday Andrea relaxes. She stays home all day. She is working hard to be a sports player.

New Words

glove

badminton

racket

goggles

10 minutes

Part A. Sentence Completion

1. Andrea ________ badminton.

(A) play
(B) plays
(C) is play
(D) playing

2. ________ is the pool? It is near my school.

(A) Who
(B) Why
(C) What
(D) Where

Part B. Situational Writing

3.

She takes a ________ to the court.

(A) bat
(B) ball
(C) ticket
(D) racket

4.

He is a ________.

(A) driver
(B) golfer
(C) pitcher
(D) swimmer

5. How many students play badminton twice a week?

(A) 2
(B) 10
(C) 13
(D) 15

6. How many students do NOT play badminton twice a week?

(A) 2
(B) 15
(C) 28
(D) 30

Part D. **General Reading and Retelling**

Andrea wants to be a sports player. Does she like only one sport? No, she loves many sports! She loves badminton, baseball, and swimming. She practices sports every day. She plays baseball three times a week. Every Monday, Wednesday, and Friday, she goes to the school playground. She carries a baseball glove and a ball. She is a baseball pitcher. She plays badminton twice a week. Where is she on Tuesdays and Thursdays? She is at the badminton court. She brings her racket. What about Saturday? Saturday is swimming day. She goes to the pool near her school. She always wears swimming goggles. Every Sunday Andrea relaxes. She stays home all day. She is working hard to be a sports player.

7. What is the best title?

(A) Andrea Stays Home
(B) Andrea Loves Sports
(C) Andrea Wants Water
(D) Andrea Loses Her Glove

8. Which sport does Andrea NOT do?

(A) skating
(B) baseball
(C) swimming
(D) badminton

9. Where is Andrea on Fridays?

(A) at a pool
(B) on a beach
(C) on a badminton court
(D) at her school's playground

10. What does Andrea wear on Saturdays?

(A) a baseball glove
(B) a bicycle helmet
(C) basketball shorts
(D) swimming goggles

Listening Practice

Listen and write.

MP3 S1-9

Andrea Loves Sports

Andrea wants to be a sports player. Does she like only one sport? No, she loves many sports! She loves [1] , baseball, and swimming. She practices sports every day. She plays baseball three times a week. Every Monday, Wednesday, and Friday, she goes to the school playground. She carries a baseball [2] and a ball. She is a baseball pitcher. She plays badminton twice a week. Where is she on Tuesdays and Thursdays? She is at the badminton court. She brings her [3] . What about Saturday? Saturday is swimming day. She goes to the pool near her school. She always wears swimming [4] . Every Sunday Andrea relaxes. She stays home all day. She is working hard to be a sports player.

Word Bank

racket	lacket
goggles	gogles
glub	glove
badminton	vadminton

Listen. Pause. Say each sentence.

MP3 S1-9G

Writing Practice

Write the words.

1

2

3

4

Write the words.

Summary

Andrea loves many ________________. She loves badminton, baseball, and swimming. She practices sports every day.

Word Puzzle

I	I	S	E	C	H	W	N	I	C	T	H	I	T	S
A	U	J	F	L	E	L	P	C	M	D	X	A	P	Y
A	B	P	A	Z	F	V	X	E	Q	Z	S	R	E	D
J	K	X	C	G	W	V	F	Q	A	L	G	G	T	O
A	X	P	F	T	P	I	U	S	Q	J	Z	C	Q	I
F	E	E	O	K	L	R	E	J	R	A	C	K	E	T
F	J	J	Y	Y	J	I	R	P	B	R	F	Y	J	Y
O	M	L	B	E	D	B	R	O	H	W	Z	I	C	Z
B	G	O	G	G	L	E	S	R	V	S	N	E	F	I
W	L	B	Z	T	Y	O	Q	D	G	H	O	H	I	I
Y	O	F	S	F	B	D	F	J	O	G	W	M	L	A
G	V	M	F	V	W	H	Z	S	Z	S	J	S	J	R
M	E	W	L	G	W	B	A	D	M	I	N	T	O	N
L	Y	U	X	K	M	V	A	S	X	B	G	D	W	V
S	B	M	I	W	G	C	V	T	M	C	P	W	S	A

Write the words. Then find them in the puzzle.

1 ____________

2 ____________

3 ____________

4 ____________

Teacher's Book p.81

UNIT 10

Alec Gets Sick in Winter

Think! Your friend has a cold.
You say: "Wear ___________. Eat ___________.
Drink ___________."

UNIT 10 Alec Gets Sick in Winter

Winter is coming soon. It is cold outside. Does Alec wear warm clothes? No, he wears thin clothes. And he has no hat on his head. So Alec gets sick. He has a fever. He sneezes and coughs. He has a sore throat. Today is Thursday. But Alec cannot go to school. He goes to the doctor. The doctor asks, "How do you feel?" Alec says, "I have a fever. I sneeze and cough. I feel very sick." The doctor says, "You have to wear warm clothes. It's cold outside. Take this medicine twice a day. Eat hot soup. Stay in bed." Alec goes home. He takes the medicine. He gets into bed. He stays under a thick blanket. Poor Alec!

New Words

fever

cough

sneeze

sore throat

10 minutes

Part A. Sentence Completion

1. ________ he wear a hat?

(A) Is
(B) Who
(C) Does
(D) What

2. He cannot go ________ school today. He is sick.

(A) at
(B) in
(C) to
(D) for

Part B. Situational Writing

3.

My mother is a ________.

(A) baker
(B) driver
(C) doctor
(D) banker

4.

Wear ________ clothes.

(A) wet
(B) red
(C) thin
(D) warm

Medicine	When	Why
	before lunch	fever
	after dinner	cough
	at night	headache
	in the morning	sore throat

5. Which medicine is for a sore throat?

(A)

(B)

(C)

(D)

6. Jason takes medicine at night. What is his problem?

(A) a fever
(B) a cough
(C) a headache
(D) a sore throat

Part D. General Reading and Retelling

Winter is coming soon. It is cold outside. Does Alec wear warm clothes? No, he wears thin clothes. And he has no hat on his head. So Alec gets sick. He has a fever. He sneezes and coughs. He has a sore throat. Today is Thursday. But Alec cannot go to school. He goes to the doctor. The doctor asks, “How do you feel?” Alec says, “I have a fever. I sneeze and cough. I feel very sick.” The doctor says, “You have to wear warm clothes. It’s cold outside. Take this medicine twice a day. Eat hot soup. Stay in bed.” Alec goes home. He takes the medicine. He gets into bed. He stays under a thick blanket. Poor Alec!

7. What is Alec’s problem?

(A) a hurt ear
(B) a bad tooth
(C) a sore throat
(D) a broken leg

8. Why is Alec sick?

(A) dirty hands
(B) thin clothes
(C) a late bedtime
(D) too much ice cream

9. Where does Alec go on Thursday?

(A) to school
(B) to a market
(C) to the doctor
(D) to the dentist

10. What does Alec’s doctor say?

(A) Go to school.
(B) Eat more salad.
(C) Wear warm clothes.
(D) Take medicine once a week.

Listening Practice

Listen and write.

MP3 S1-10

Alec Gets Sick in Winter

Winter is coming soon. It is cold outside. Does Alec wear warm clothes? No, he wears thin clothes. And he has no hat on his head. So Alec gets sick. He has a [1] ________ . He sneezes and [2] ________ . He has a [3] ________ . Today is Thursday. But Alec cannot go to school. He goes to the doctor. The doctor asks, "How do you feel?" Alec says, "I have a fever. I [4] ________ and cough. I feel very sick." The doctor says, "You have to wear warm clothes. It's cold outside. Take this medicine twice a day. Eat hot soup. Stay in bed." Alec goes home. He takes the medicine. He gets into bed. He stays under a thick blanket. Poor Alec!

Word Bank

sneeze	feber
coughs	sore throat
sniz	sore trot
fever	coffs

Listen. Pause. Say each sentence.

MP3 S1-10G

Writing Practice

Write the words.

1

2

3

4

Write the words.

Summary

It is winter. Alec does not wear warm clothes. He gets ______________.

He sees a doctor. Alec takes medicine and goes to bed.

Word Puzzle

Q	H	F	N	Q	Z	C	E	U	Z	Q	A	U	Y	C
M	U	B	C	O	O	O	A	S	N	E	E	Z	E	S
O	G	U	U	S	M	U	B	N	A	A	O	S	C	I
N	A	Y	X	A	Z	G	X	H	O	Z	R	R	B	A
L	Q	U	H	A	V	H	F	Z	V	C	Q	N	T	E
F	P	I	I	C	J	G	J	P	C	Y	V	B	X	P
O	Y	Q	D	A	S	O	R	E	T	H	R	O	A	T
Y	I	A	M	J	S	H	W	J	I	Q	Z	M	I	Z
C	R	D	K	Z	Q	F	U	P	L	I	D	V	R	V
V	T	P	U	L	P	E	C	U	U	Q	F	B	H	O
A	U	X	B	E	Q	V	D	C	K	O	G	Q	Y	W
Z	L	Z	V	T	O	E	J	P	Y	I	M	T	U	Y
V	A	T	J	Y	T	R	I	S	B	S	D	R	I	R
Z	V	D	J	Z	D	L	V	P	W	K	P	S	U	E
I	B	N	P	N	J	Q	E	F	J	F	G	H	W	C

Write the words. Then find them in the puzzle.

1 ____________

2 ____________

3 ____________

4 ____________

Teacher's Book p.85

UNIT 11

Mr. Wind and Mr. Sun

Who is stronger? Is it the sun? Or is it the wind?

UNIT 11 Mr. Wind and Mr. Sun

Mr. Wind and Mr. Sun fight. Mr. Wind says, "I am stronger!" Mr. Sun says, "No! I am stronger!" They see a man. Mr. Wind says, "That man has a red jacket. Let's take off his jacket. Can I do it? Then I am the strongest. Can you do it? Then you are the strongest." Mr. Sun says, "Okay!" Mr. Wind tries first. He blows hard. But the man gets colder. He keeps his jacket on. Mr. Wind tries again. He blows harder. But the man keeps his jacket on. Mr. Wind gets angry. Now Mr. Sun tries. He starts to shine. The day gets warmer. Finally, the man takes off the jacket. Mr. Sun says, "You see? I am stronger than you."

New Words

fight

jacket

strong

take off

10 minutes

Part A. Sentence Completion

1. This is ________ plan.

   (A) I
   (B) my
   (C) me
   (D) mine

2. He ________ again.

   (A) try
   (B) tries
   (C) to try
   (D) trying

Part B. Situational Writing

3.

He ________ his socks and shoes.

(A) buys
(B) slides
(C) puts on
(D) takes off

4.

Our dad is ________.

(A) cold
(B) weak
(C) angry
(D) strong

Part C. Practical Reading and Retelling

Get a stronger mind!

What: Central Reading Club

Where: Central Library

How: Read one book.

The library gives you one sticker.

Get 20 stickers. Then get one free pencil!

5. What can you get in the club?

(A) 20 free pencils
(B) a thicker jacket
(C) a stronger mind
(D) 10 sticker books

6. Where is the club?

(A) at a gym
(B) at a library
(C) at a sticker shop
(D) at a pencil store

Part D. **General Reading and Retelling**

Mr. Wind and Mr. Sun fight. Mr. Wind says, "I am stronger!" Mr. Sun says, "No! I am stronger!" They see a man. Mr. Wind says, "That man has a red jacket. Let's take off his jacket. Can I do it? Then I am the strongest. Can you do it? Then you are the strongest." Mr. Sun says, "Okay!" Mr. Wind tries first. He blows hard. But the man gets colder. He keeps his jacket on. Mr. Wind tries again. He blows harder. But the man keeps his jacket on. Mr. Wind gets angry. Now Mr. Sun tries. He starts to shine. The day gets warmer. Finally, the man takes off the jacket. Mr. Sun says, "You see? I am stronger than you."

7. What is Mr. Wind's question?

(A) Who is faster?
(B) Who is bigger?
(C) Who is kinder?
(D) Who is stronger?

8. What is the man wearing?

(A) a blue hat
(B) a red jacket
(C) a green coat
(D) a purple scarf

9. What does Mr. Wind do?

(A) blow out air
(B) put on a hat
(C) take a jacket
(D) carry the man

10. How does Mr. Sun win?

(A) He jumps.
(B) He shines.
(C) He gets cold.
(D) He blows hard.

Listening Practice

Listen and write.

MP3 S1-11

Mr. Wind and Mr. Sun

Mr. Wind and Mr. Sun 1 ______. Mr. Wind says, "I am 2 ______!" Mr. Sun says, "No! I am stronger!" They see a man. Mr. Wind says, "That man has a red 3 ______. Let's take off his jacket. Can I do it? Then I am the strongest. Can you do it? Then you are the strongest." Mr. Sun says, "Okay!" Mr. Wind tries first. He blows hard. But the man gets colder. He keeps his jacket on. Mr. Wind tries again. He blows harder. But the man keeps his jacket on. Mr. Wind gets angry. Now Mr. Sun tries. He starts to shine. The day gets warmer. Finally, the man 4 ______ the jacket. Mr. Sun says, "You see? I am stronger than you."

Word Bank

jaket	stranger
pite	jacket
takes of	takes off
stronger	fight

Listen. Pause. Say each sentence.

MP3 S1-11G

Writing Practice

Write the words.

1

2

3

4

Write the words.

Summary

Mr. Wind and Mr. Sun ________________. Who is stronger? They have a contest. Mr. Sun wins.

Word Puzzle

C	A	P	T	B	B	G	A	P	M	N	L	T	K	E
P	G	Y	V	N	K	P	M	H	F	Z	F	X	Q	G
Z	O	M	A	X	V	G	P	V	U	Y	I	Y	V	M
U	W	A	U	I	Y	S	U	E	A	D	G	A	J	Z
P	W	K	B	D	J	T	U	Y	J	E	H	R	A	I
L	S	F	Y	Q	X	C	L	S	Q	X	T	Z	C	U
Z	T	O	O	W	H	P	X	B	P	N	R	Y	K	G
N	R	R	Y	I	O	T	D	D	E	O	L	C	E	E
R	O	O	V	P	I	B	P	Y	B	V	T	M	T	K
N	N	E	O	E	V	S	O	S	Y	X	A	S	M	I
R	G	V	W	K	P	D	T	E	U	O	K	Y	V	W
P	Q	H	G	K	X	J	W	G	L	G	E	I	P	L
V	P	N	Z	G	Y	O	G	J	Y	U	O	V	C	L
M	G	N	S	C	H	B	Y	E	X	M	F	Z	M	B
L	Q	Q	B	I	W	G	Y	E	H	K	F	S	P	Z

Write the words. Then find them in the puzzle.

1 ______________ 2 ______________ 3 ______________ 4 ______________

Teacher's Book p.89

UNIT 12

At the Theme Park

Do you like theme parks? Look at the picture.
Which rides are fun? Which rides are scary?

UNIT 12 At the Theme Park

Why are Lucy and Mona excited? Today they have a school field trip! All the students are going to a theme park. It is the biggest one in Korea. There are many great rides. There are also some scary rides. But Lucy and Mona are brave. They are trying every ride. They run to the water ride. But the line is long. The friends wait for an hour. They get to the front of the line. But there is a problem. They cannot get on the ride. Why not? They are too short. The friends are sad. Where can they go? They can go on the teddy bear ride. It is not the water ride. It is not scary. But it is a long ride. And the teddy bear cars are cute. Lucy and Mona have fun.

New Words

ride

scary

front

brave

Part A. Sentence Completion

1. They ________ brave.

   (A) is
   (B) are
   (C) can
   (D) being

2. There are many great ________.

   (A) ride
   (B) rides
   (C) a ride
   (D) our ride

Part B. Situational Writing

3.

The students are on a ________ trip.

(A) field
(B) family
(C) bicycle
(D) business

4.

Ken's shirt is green. Ken is at the ________ of the line.

(A) back
(B) front
(C) bottom
(D) middle

Favorite Rides

Student	Ride	Why
Ben	Robot Ride	Modern!
Ara	Water Ride	Scary! I like scary rides.
Junho	Teddy Bear Ride	Cute!
Martin	Rainbow Ride	Many colors!

5. Who likes scary rides?

   (A) Ben
   (B) Ara
   (C) Junho
   (D) Martin

6. Why does Martin like the Rainbow Ride?

   (A) It is very cute.
   (B) It is very scary.
   (C) It is very modern.
   (D) It has many colors.

Part D. General Reading and Retelling

Why are Lucy and Mona excited? Today they have a school field trip! All the students are going to a theme park. It is the biggest one in Korea. There are many great rides. There are also some scary rides. But Lucy and Mona are brave. They are trying every ride. They run to the water ride. But the line is long. The friends wait for an hour. They get to the front of the line. But there is a problem. They cannot get on the ride. Why not? They are too short. The friends are sad. Where can they go? They can go on the teddy bear ride. It is not the water ride. It is not scary. But it is a long ride. And the teddy bear cars are cute. Lucy and Mona have fun.

7. What is the best title?

(A) Lucy's Big Fight
(B) How to Ride a Bike
(C) At the Theme Park
(D) Lucy and Mona in Class

8. Where are Lucy and Mona going today?

(A) to school
(B) to a museum
(C) to a water park
(D) to a theme park

9. Who goes on the water ride?

(A) no one
(B) only Lucy
(C) Lucy and Mona
(D) Lucy, Mona, and their teacher

10. What is true about the teddy bear ride?

(A) It is long.
(B) It is short.
(C) It is scary.
(D) It is closed.

Listening Practice

Listen and write.

MP3 S1-12

At the Theme Park

Why are Lucy and Mona excited? Today they have a school field trip! All the students are going to a theme park. It is the biggest one in Korea. There are many great [1] ____________. There are also some [2] ____________ rides. But Lucy and Mona are [3] ____________. They are trying every ride. They run to the water ride. But the line is long. The friends wait for an hour. They get to the [4] ____________ of the line. But there is a problem. They cannot get on the ride. Why not? They are too short. The friends are sad. Where can they go? They can go on the teddy bear ride. It is not the water ride. It is not scary. But it is a long ride. And the teddy bear cars are cute. Lucy and Mona have fun.

Word Bank

frant	breve
front	scary
brave	rides
lides	skary

Listen. Pause. Say each sentence.

MP3 S1-12G

Writing Practice

Write the words.

1

2

3

4

Write the words.

Summary

Lucy and Mona go to a ________________. They cannot get on the water ride. But they can go on the teddy bear ride. They have fun.

Word Puzzle

L	U	J	L	K	N	Y	I	Y	B	R	C	A	V	Y
C	G	P	D	F	M	Q	F	P	P	Y	P	O	S	P
R	K	L	Z	A	H	E	L	I	I	D	B	K	R	C
L	F	Y	W	N	E	B	L	Y	O	U	S	N	J	C
R	F	F	W	V	J	W	E	V	Q	K	C	O	K	C
D	N	I	E	E	H	Y	M	T	E	P	A	E	H	Q
E	B	X	J	P	E	H	R	X	M	U	R	K	C	T
A	X	X	B	Q	A	R	I	Q	Y	B	Y	U	X	C
L	I	F	G	N	B	V	D	X	Y	T	X	U	F	K
K	B	F	X	A	R	K	E	Q	L	V	M	J	D	J
O	T	X	Q	U	A	T	A	W	S	A	Y	N	A	Q
T	Q	Y	T	X	V	O	Q	M	G	C	T	R	Z	F
Y	H	H	H	B	E	V	N	N	V	H	L	Z	Q	T
F	R	H	F	J	R	G	C	D	S	C	G	K	C	I
F	R	O	N	T	L	E	E	R	I	U	N	W	E	P

Write the words. Then find them in the puzzle.

1 ____________

2 ____________

3 ____________

4 ____________

CHAPTER REVIEW

Match the pictures to the correct words.

Teacher's Book p.93

badminton

brave

cough

fever

fight

front

glove

goggles

jacket

racket

ride

scary

sneeze

sore throat

strong

take off

ANSWERS

CHAPTER 1 | Weekend Activities
p.10

UNIT 1	1 (B)	2 (B)	3 (C)	4 (B)	5 (D)	6 (C)	7 (B)	8 (B)	9 (A)	10 (A)
S1-1	1 wake up		2 screams		3 dries		4 packs			
p.11	1 wake up		2 scream		3 pack a bag		4 dry		goes to bed	
	1 wake up		2 scream		3 pack a bag		4 dry			
UNIT 2	1 (A)	2 (C)	3 (D)	4 (B)	5 (D)	6 (D)	7 (D)	8 (B)	9 (B)	10 (B)
S1-2	1 headphones		2 bakes		3 photos		4 phone			
p.19	1 phone		2 headphones		3 bake		4 take photos		Sunday	
	1 phone		2 headphones		3 bake		4 take photos			
UNIT 3	1 (B)	2 (A)	3 (D)	4 (D)	5 (D)	6 (B)	7 (D)	8 (B)	9 (A)	10 (A)
S1-3	1 fresh		2 hill		3 safety		4 helmets			
p.27	1 fresh		2 hill		3 safety		4 helmet		field trip	
	1 fresh		2 hill		3 safety		4 helmet			
UNIT 4	1 (A)	2 (D)	3 (A)	4 (D)	5 (C)	6 (B)	7 (B)	8 (C)	9 (B)	10 (D)
S1-4	1 diary		2 movie		3 subway		4 amusement			
p.35	1 diary		2 movie theater		3 subway		4 amusement park		movie theater	
	1 diary		2 movie theater		3 subway		4 amusement park			

CHAPTER 2 | Find Out about Your Friends
p.44

UNIT 5	1 (B)	2 (B)	3 (C)	4 (D)	5 (B)	6 (D)	7 (D)	8 (A)	9 (B)	10 (B)
S1-5	1 pumpkins		2 vegetables		3 shells		4 holidays			
p.45	1 pumpkin		2 shell		3 vegetable		4 holiday		Pumpkins	
	1 pumpkin		2 shell		3 vegetable		4 holiday			
UNIT 6	1 (A)	2 (D)	3 (D)	4 (A)	5 (C)	6 (D)	7 (D)	8 (C)	9 (A)	10 (C)
S1-6	1 feeds		2 sweeps		3 laundry		4 trash			
p.53	1 feed		2 sweep		3 laundry		4 trash		home	
	1 feed		2 sweep		3 laundry		4 trash			
UNIT 7	1 (A)	2 (D)	3 (C)	4 (C)	5 (A)	6 (D)	7 (D)	8 (C)	9 (B)	10 (C)
S1-7	1 planning		2 fancy		3 put on		4 wait			
p.61	1 plan		2 fancy		3 put on		4 wait for		party	
	1 plan		2 fancy		3 put on		4 wait for			
UNIT 8	1 (A)	2 (B)	3 (B)	4 (D)	5 (A)	6 (A)	7 (C)	8 (C)	9 (B)	10 (A)
S1-8	1 first		2 second		3 third		4 fourth			
p.69	1 first		2 second		3 third		4 fourth		sound	
	1 first		2 second		3 third		4 fourth			

CHAPTER 3 | Ask More Questions
p.78

UNIT 9	1 (B)	2 (D)	3 (D)	4 (C)	5 (B)	6 (D)	7 (B)	8 (A)	9 (D)	10 (D)
S1-9	1 badminton		2 glove		3 racket		4 goggles			
p.79	1 glove		2 badminton		3 racket		4 goggles		sports	
	1 glove		2 badminton		3 racket		4 goggles			
UNIT 10	1 (C)	2 (C)	3 (C)	4 (D)	5 (D)	6 (C)	7 (C)	8 (B)	9 (C)	10 (C)
S1-10	1 fever		2 coughs		3 sore throat		4 sneeze			
p.87	1 fever		2 cough		3 sneeze		4 sore throat		sick	
	1 fever		2 cough		3 sneeze		4 sore throat			
UNIT 11	1 (B)	2 (B)	3 (D)	4 (D)	5 (C)	6 (B)	7 (D)	8 (B)	9 (A)	10 (B)
S1-11	1 fight		2 stronger		3 jacket		4 takes off			
p.95	1 fight		2 jacket		3 strong		4 take off		fight	
	1 fight		2 jacket		3 strong		4 take off			
UNIT 12	1 (B)	2 (B)	3 (A)	4 (B)	5 (B)	6 (D)	7 (C)	8 (D)	9 (A)	10 (A)
S1-12	1 rides		2 scary		3 brave		4 front			
p.103	1 ride		2 scary		3 front		4 brave		theme park	
	1 ride		2 scary		3 front		4 brave			

TOSEL Lab에는 어떤 콘텐츠가 있나요?

진단

맞춤형 레벨테스트로
정확한 평가 제공

Placement Test

응시자 빅데이터 분석에 기반한 테스트로 신규 상담 학생의 영어능력을 정확하게 진단하고 효과적인 영어 교육을 실시하기 위한 객관적인 가이드라인을 제공합니다.

교재

세분화된 레벨로
실력에 맞는 학습 제공

Book Content

TOSEL의 세분화된 교재 레벨은 각 연령에 맞는 어휘와 읽기 지능 및 교과 과정과의 연계가 가능하도록 설계된 교재들로 효과적인 학습 커리큘럼을 제공합니다.

자기주도학습

교재와 연계한 다양한 콘텐츠로
효과적인 학습 제공

Study Content

Monthly Test를 대비한 다양한 콘텐츠를 제공해 영어 학습에 시너지 효과를 기대할 수 있으며, 학생들의 자기주도 학습 습관을 더 탄탄하게 키울 수 있습니다.

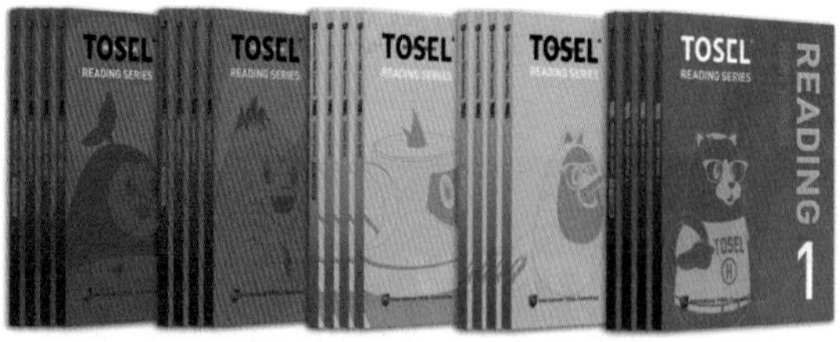

내신과 토셀 고득점을 한꺼번에!

Reading Series

Pre-Starter / Starter / Basic / Junior / High Junior

- 각 단어 학습 도입부에 주제와 관련된 이미지를 통한 말하기 연습
- 각 Unit 별 4-6개의 목표 단어 제시, 그림 또는 영문으로 단어 뜻을 제공하여 독해 학습 전 단어 숙지
- 독해&실용문 연습을 위한 지문과 Comprehension 문항을 10개씩 수록하여 이해도 확인 및 진단
- 숙지한 독해 지문을 원어민 음성으로 들으며 듣기 학습, 듣기 전, 듣기 중, 듣기 후 학습 커리큘럼 마련

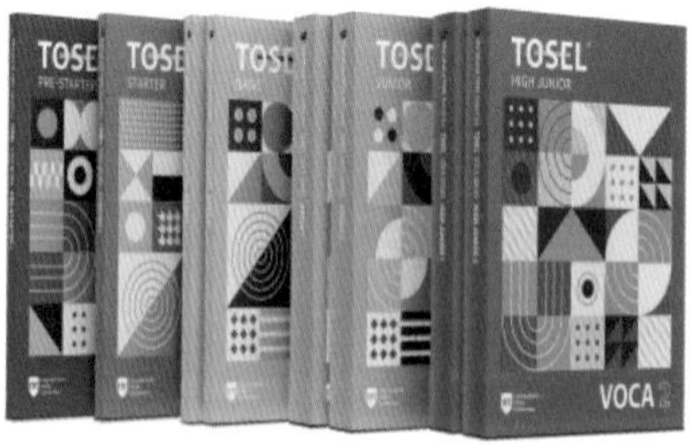

학년별 꼭 알아야하는 **단어 수록!**

Voca Series

Pre-Starter / Starter / Basic / Junior / High Junior

- 초등/중등 교과과정 연계 단어 학습과 세분화된 레벨
- TOSEL 시험을 기준으로 빈출 지표를 활용한 예문과 문제 구성
- 실제 TOSEL 지문의 예문을 활용한 실용적 학습 제공
- 실전 감각 향상과 점검을 위한 실전 문제 수록